I wish I had ears like a bat

illustrated by
Amy Bates

written by
Shelly Hurst Lonni

Did you know that a bat's big ears help it to hear, find, and catch an insect very quickly?

I wish I had ears like a bat. Then I could find the noisy cricket that keeps me awake at night.

Did you know that a porcupine has sharp quills to keep other animals away? Their quills make them quite untouchable. Ouch!

I wish I had quills like a porcupine. Then I'd have lots of room in the car. No one would want to sit by me.

Did you know that a frog can see what is behind it without turning its head? This helps it look out for danger and for food.

I wish I had eyes like a frog. Then no one
could sneak up behind me while playing tag.
I'd never have to be "It."

Did you know that a shark can smell underwater, even from far away? This helps it hunt for food to eat, like fish.

I wish I could smell as well as a shark.
Then I'd find where all the fish were hiding.
Maybe I'd catch a hundred fish!

Did you know that a butterfly has taste buds on its feet?
It walks around on a flower to find out if it's sweet.

I wish I had taste buds like a butterfly. Then I could walk on my dinner to taste it. Well, maybe not. I'd have to clean up the mess!

But being me isn't so bad. I can see to read a book.
I can hear the wind blow. I can smell cookies baking.
I can feel my cat's soft fur. And I can taste this yummy
ice cream. Mmm . . .